RESCUE DOGS
A COLORING BOOK

@cm.books

 @cm.coloringbooks

ISBN-13: 978-1735546513
ISBN-10: 1735546518

Who Rescued Who?

This book is dedicated to my rescue dog, Ember (see cover). Em was rescued from Korean K9 Rescue in June 2019, just about one year after a freak lung complication left me in the hospital for roughly two weeks. To put into perspective my extreme desire to be a dog mom, when I was waiting for the ambulance to pick me up from urgent care, I turned to my partner and said "if I survive this, we are getting a dog."

Upon returning home, I suffered from crippling anxiety for many months—I was diagnosed with Generalized Anxiety Disorder (GAD) and a mild case of PTSD. Though less severe and less often, I still struggle with anxiety from time to time and having Ember has immeasurably helped me through these tough days. She has completely changed my life and I am incredibly thankful for Korean K9 Rescue—and the many rescue organizations worldwide—who make this kind of unconditional love possible for so many people.

The dogs depicted in this coloring book have been saved, rehabilitated, and loved by twelve organizations from across the United States. For each month of 2021, I will be donating 50% of royalties to each of the featured rescues.

Table of Contents

KOREAN K9 RESCUE

We are a non-profit, No-Kill 501©(3) dog rescue organization that saves dogs from the meat trade, puppy mills, and high-kill shelters in South Korea. Due to the stigma associated with mixed-breed dogs and those from dog meat farms, most dogs have a low chance of being adopted in South Korea and run the risk of being euthanized. We transport at-risk dogs to the United States, where we place them in loving forever homes. Through this process, we can spread awareness about the brutal dog meat trade and advocate for the voiceless dogs that are still suffering.

www.koreank9rescue.org
info@koreank9rescue.org
 @koreank9rescue

Mango

Buddy

Donghae

Ember

DoVE Project (Dogs of Violence Exposed) is a non-profit organization focused on supporting the end of the dog meat trade in S. Korea. Through diligent rescue efforts, activism and education within the country, a future where the slaughtering of dogs for human consumption is eliminated is possible.

www.dove-project.org
info@dove-project.org
 @doveanddogs
 @dove_project

Appa

TREATS 10¢

Journey

Rocco

The Animal Pad is a non-profit, all breed dog rescue that focuses on saving dogs from high kill shelters and the streets of Mexico.

We get them vet care, place them in foster homes and then find them loving forever families. A few years ago, we turned our attention to the street dogs of Mexico as there is very little help for them. Since then, we have developed a large rescue network in Baja California and we have a sister shelter in Ensenada that we focus on taking dogs from whenever funds allow.

www.theanimalpad.org
info@theanimalpad.com
 @TheAnimalPad

WOOF

WOOF WOOF

WOOF DOOF

WOOF WOOF

DOOF

WOOF WOOF

WOOF

Kung Pao

Benji

TACOS

Portobello

Rescue. Train. Educate. Adopt.

Northwest Dog Project rescues, re-homes and enhances the lives of neglected, abused and homeless dogs, while advocating responsible pet ownership. We welcome medically-challenged dogs and provide a nurturing forever sanctuary to seniors who have been abandoned in their golden years.

www.northwestdogproject.org
info@northwestdogproject.org
@ @nwdogproject

Wesley

DOG TOYS

Franklin

Fritz

Benson

Simply Southern Rescue

Ren Dowhaniuk (who has since moved and is no longer active with the rescue), and Leigh Ann Albritton worked together over the past two years and saved, along with a network of others, over 650 animals, all relocated to safe and stable homes. We believe that all animals deserve a safe home and stable life. We are a rescue that is not based on a specific breed, but rather a direct need. Cats, dogs, pigs, opossums ... if we see an animal in need, we try our best to help. Our primary focus is helping strays in the parish and surrounding areas, but we love the opportunity to pull from the Humane Society of Monroe, Ruston Animal Control, 4Paws Rescue, and OPAS.

www.simplysouthernrescue.com
simplysouthernrescue@gmail.com
 @caninesorfelines
 @southern2426

Buddy

Chance

Grace

big fluffy dog RESCUE

Big Fluffy Dog Rescue is a 501©(3) organization dedicated to helping giant breed mixed breed dogs in need. We value dogs of all breeds, but we specialize in what the name says: big, fluffy dogs. We have volunteers from the Rocky Mountains to the Atlantic Ocean and the Gulf of Mexico to Canada who work to help homeless big fluffy dogs find a home to call their own. Big Fluffy Dog Rescue works to save Great Pyrenees, Saint Bernards, Newfoundlands and their mixes from euthanasia. We also have a fair assortment of honorary fluffies who don't fall into the traditional fluffy mold but are with us anyway and we love their tiny/non-fluffy selves as much as the others.

www.bigfluffydogs.com
jean@bigfluffydogs.com
⊙ⓕ @bigfluffydogrescue

Baladev

Twinkie

PUPPIES ON PARADE

Cerdwyn

PAWS ABOARD

Gotham

Great Plains SPCA is one of the largest no-kill animal shelters in Kansas City, serving nearly 6,000 pets annually. Located in Merriam, Kansas, our mission is to drive change in our community through innovative programs that promote adoption, outreach and a better life for pets and the people who love them. We are an independent 501©(3) nonprofit that proudly reports a live-release rate of 97% or higher.

www.greatplainsspca.org
⊙ⓕ🐦 @GreatPlainsSPCA

Queen

Monty

Cronus

Zuma

Big Dog Ranch Rescue, the largest cage-free no kill shelter, was founded on the idea that every dog deserves to live and, most importantly, to live a full and happy life. We are devoted to creating a healing community for dogs, both big and small, who have been neglected, abandoned, and mistreated.

www.bdrr.org
saveadog@bdrr.org
⚪🄵 **@bigdogranchrescue**

SALOON

Garnet

JACKPOT

Mouse

Shep

The Sato Project

The Sato Project is dedicated to rescuing abused and abandoned dogs from Puerto Rico. The organization is committed to fostering long-term change for the satos in Puerto Rico through ongoing rescue efforts and through their community Spay, Neuter, Vaccine and Microchip Program. There are an estimated 500,000 stray dogs on the island, but through these programs, as well as community outreach and education, TSP is working toward a future where every dog is humanely cared for. They have rescued, rehabilitated and found homes for over 5,000 dogs since 2011 and a major part of their mission is to permanently change public perception of these incredible dogs.

www.thesatoproject.org
⭘ ⓕ 𝕏 @TheSatoProject

US BOUND

SPECIAL
DELIVERY

Tass

Ariel

Airsong's Angels, Inc is an all volunteer, 501©3 nonprofit organization and Georgia State Licensed Animal Rescue dedicated to improving the lives of the vizslas in our care by: bringing them current on vaccinations, attending to their medical and behavioral needs, providing for spay/neuter, and carefully rehoming them into loving, furever families.

www.airsongsangelsinc.org
airsongsangels@gmail.com
⓪ @airsongs.angels.inc
❶ @airsongsangelsinc

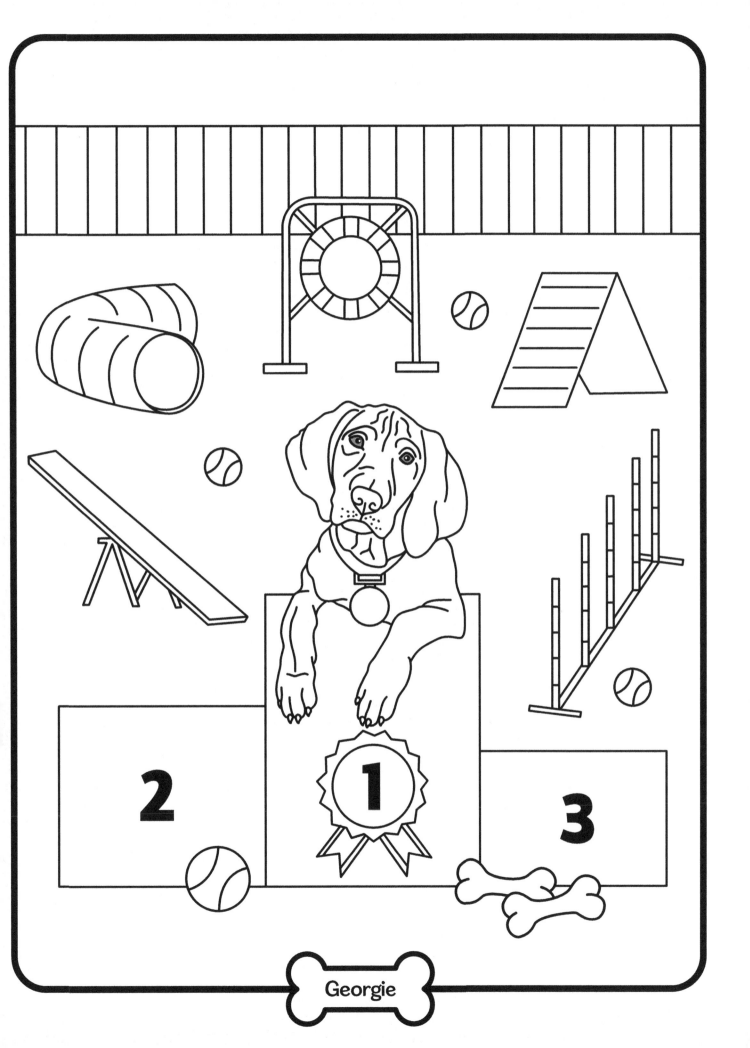

Georgie

Millie

Harry

Hazel

Dallas Dog RESCUES the hurt and abandoned, REHABILITATES the broken and REFORMS the community through education to eliminate animal neglect.

Dallas Dog Rescue Rehab Reform is a group of dedicated animal loving volunteers that help rescue dogs with our main focus being SE Dallas.

www.dallasdogrrr.org
hello@dallasdogrrr.org
 @DallasDogRRR
 @dallasdog_rescue_rehab_reform

Mr. Ed Ducky

Sly McFly

Perkins

Serenity
and Harold

Passion 4 Paws' Mission is to rescue homeless, abandoned, neglected or abused dogs primarily from the South where there are thousands of dogs in need. By working with committed Fosters, Volunteers, Supporters, Adopters, Veterinarians, and Trainers both in Vermont and in the South, we will rescue, nurture, provide medical care, housing, and rehabilitation to these precious pups while providing a safe and loving environment for as long as it takes for their families to find and Adopt them in to their forever homes.

www.passion-4-paws.org
InquiriesPassion4PawsVT@gmail.com
⊙ ⓕ @passion4pawsvt

Mikey

Luna

Snoopy

Max

Color Test Page

Thank You

Thank you to the twelve organizations featured in this book—and all rescue organizations worldwide—for the extraordinary work that you do every day to help animals in need. I would also like to thank the volunteers whose time and dedication is paramount to many rescue organization's success. Lastly, I'd like to thank all the rescue dog parents and dog lovers out there who support rescue organizations and advocate for the well-being of our beloved fur babies!

Made in the USA
Coppell, TX
19 October 2021